REALM OF THE DAMNED

TENEBRIS DEOS

PART I

HELL'S
HUNGER

I NEVER RATTED ON YOU, IF THAT'S WHAT YOU THINK. I CAME HERE SO'S WE COULD BURN THIS PLACE *TOGETHER*... FOR US... FOR THE *BAND*...

WE DIDN'T COME HERE TO TORCH A *CHURCH*, KRISTOFFER.

WE CAME HERE TO TORCH THE WHOLE FUCKING *WORLD!*

HOLD HIM.

LARS! MARKUS! *LISTEN* TO ME. WE'VE KNOWN EACH OTHER SINCE WE WERE *KIDS*.

YOU DON'T *BELIEVE* ALL HIS CONSPIRACY SHIT ABOUT MONSTERS RULING THE WORLD! C'MON!

UHN! DON'T LEAVE! I'LL DO WHATEVER YOU WANT...

WHAT ABOUT THE POLICE, TOMAS?

I'M GONNA CALL THEM MYSELF.

I CAN'T WAIT TO SEE THEIR FACES WHEN THEY GET HERE. HAHAHA!

PLEASE...

TOMAS, ARE YOU SURE THIS IS GOING TO WORK?

WE'VE COME TOO FAR FOR YOU TO START HAVING DOUBTS, LARS. YOU THINK THAT ANTIQUES DEALER WAS LYING ABOUT THE MASK? AFTER WHAT *MARKUS* DID TO HIM?

HAVE FAITH, MY FRIEND. WE'RE THE *SONS OF BALAUR*. WE'RE PART OF A CULT THAT HAS ENDURED FOR *CENTURIES*.

AND WHEN WE AWAKEN OUR *MASTER* HE WILL MAKE US HIS *SKALL* HOWLING SONGS AT HIS SI AS HE SCOURGES THE WORLD.

INVOCATION BY SONS OF BALAUR

AUDITE VOCATIONIS, GREAT BALAUR

INVOCATION
Sons of Balaur

THE MOUNTAING CROWN THE HOUSE OF PETROVA... ♪ FROM WHOSE BLACK GATES RIDES THE VOICE OF FIRE!

♪ HIS SWORD IS DRAWN AND SHEATHED IN BLOOD... ♫ CRIMSON OCEANS UNQUENCHABLE!

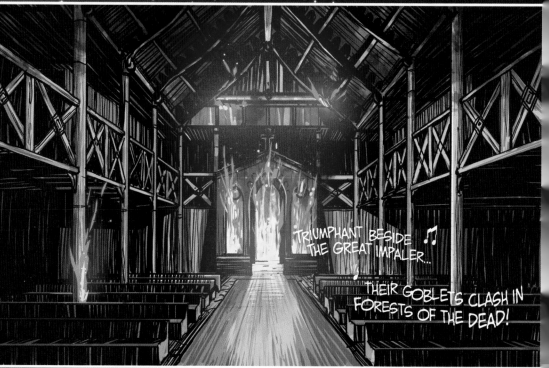

TRIUMPHANT BESIDE ♫ THE GREAT IMPALER... THEIR GOBLETS CLASH IN FORESTS OF THE DEAD!

NO! NO!

ARMOURED WITH HATE, WILD DRAGON OF HELL... ♪ UNDONE BY HOLY WORDS AND TREACHERY! ♪

♫ HIS SLEEP IS AT AN END!

!?!

SNAK!

AAAAAAAH

VZZZZz

YOU WILL REMAIN CALM, YOUNG MAN, AND FOCUS ON THE SOUND OF MY VOICE, WHICH IS ALL YOU CAN HEAR... ALL YOU CAN HEAR...

TK TK TK TK

AKK!

IN A MOMENT I WILL COUNT BACKWARDS FROM FIVE AND YOU WILL LOSE CONSCIOUSNESS.

WHEN YOU AWAKEN YOU WILL HAVE NO MEMORY OF EITHER MYSELF OR THIS YOUNG WOMAN. YOU WILL CONCLUDE THAT YOUR LINGERING DISORIENTATION HAS BEEN CAUSED BY A COMBINATION OF NARCOTICS AND ALCOHOL. YOU WILL THEN GO ABOUT YOUR LIFE.

FIVE...

FOUR...

THREE...

TW

"ONE!"

UHH?

I LEFT IT TOO LATE THIS TIME. NOW THE *HUNGER* IS UPON ME.

MY HANDS ARE TREMBLING SO MUCH I CANNOT KEEP THE NEEDLE STEADY.

MUST FIND THIS CREATURE'S VEIN BEFORE THE SUN DESTROYS THE BODY.

THERE! THANK GOD I NO LONGER HAVE TO COOK IT.

CREATING A *COMPOUND* WAS TROUBLESOME ENOUGH, EVEN WHEN I HAD THE *LABORATORY*.

MY BODY MUST BE *ADAPTING*, LIKE THAT OF ANY HUNTED ANIMAL.

FORGIVE ME, LORD.

A CENTURY OF ADDICTION DOES NOTHING TO LESSEN THE RUSH.

THE STOLEN BLOOD MELTS INTO ME, SOFTENING THE STIFFNESS IN MY JOINTS, ILLUMINATING THE DARKNESS OF THE WORLD. THEN THE LIVES OF THE CREATURE'S VICTIMS FLASH BEFORE MY EYES...

FASCINATING HOW THE VAMPIRE APPEARS TO ABSORB SOME PORTION OF THE SOUL WHEN IT FEEDS. BUT ITS MIND IS COLD AND PREDATORY, AND SO THE EXPERIENCE WASHES OVER IT LIKE A STREAM OVER STONES.

ALAS, I AM BUT MORTAL, AND MY MIND FILLS WITH FOREIGN MEMORIES UNTIL I CAN BARELY DISTINGUISH MY OWN.

AND ANOTHER PART OF ME FALLS AWAY LIKE A HANDFUL OF DEAD LEAVES.

I RECALL BEING SOMETHING OF A PHILOSOPHER IN MY YOUTH.

I WONDER WHAT THAT YOUNG MAN WOULD HAVE MADE OF *THIS* ENQUIRY: WHEN A MAN ABANDONS HIMSELF TO DUTY, WHAT THEN REMAINS OF THE MAN...?

WHAT DOES HE BECOME...?

WHAT FORCE NOW DRIVES HIM...?

I WISH TO CONFESS MY WEAKNESS, FATHER.

FORGIVE ME, FATHER, FOR I HAVE SINNED. IT HAS BEEN ONE MONTH SINCE MY LAST CONFESSION.

I CAME TO THIS COUNTRY SEEKING OTHER SURVIVORS, THINKING THERE MAY BE SOME WAY WE COULD RALLY AND SAVE THE WORLD FROM DAMNATION.

BUT I HAVE FOUND NO ONE. IT APPEARS I ALONE HAVE SURVIVED.

AND NOW IT IS ONLY A MATTER OF TIME BEFORE THE AGENTS OF DARKNESS FIND ME AND WHEN THEY DO I CAN EXPECT NO MERCY.

INDEED, THE SERPENT HIMSELF COULD NOT CONCEIVE THE TORMENTS THAT AWAIT ME SHOULD I FALL INTO THEIR HANDS.

AND YET, DESPITE THE HORRORS THAT AWAIT ME, I AM RESOLVED TO CONTINUE UNTIL THE LORD HIMSELF SEES FIT TO TAKE ME.

MY WEAKNESS IS IN TAKING GOD'S RETICENCE FOR *CRUELTY*, FATHER.

I HAVE FOLLOWED HIM FAITHFULLY FOR TWICE THE MORTAL SPAN OF YEARS, DEGRADED MY BODY IN HIS SERVICE. I HAVE ENDURED *SO MUCH* FOR HIM, FATHER, COMMITTED SO MANY... *ABHORRENT* ACTS IN HIS NAME. WHY DOES HE LET ME *ENDURE* SO?

I HAVE SEEN *MIRACLES* PERFORMED ON THIS EARTH AND YET HE ABSTAINS FROM ANSWERING *MY* PRAYERS. AND I FIND MYSELF *HATING* HIM FOR IT.

SK AASH

I AM SORRY FOR THIS AND FOR ALL OF MY SINS.

FUCKING VAMPIRES.

HURRRR!

HUK!
HUK!

I MUST MAKE SURE NOT TO LEAVE A TRAIL.

FORTUNATELY THE WOUND WILL NOT TAKE LONG TO HEAL, ANOTHER BENEFIT OF MY ADDICTION.

ALSO, I KNOW THESE TUNNELS AS WELL AS ANY RAT.

I SCURRY DOWN A NEXUS OF PASSAGES LONG FORGOTTEN, WRIGGLING BETWEEN THE ROOTS OF THE WORLD.

THE CONGREGATION WERE ADEPT AT SECRECY.

FOR CENTURIES WE DEFENDED MANKIND, BATTLED MONSTERS IN THE SHADOWS.

BASILICA OF ST ALEXA, VATICAN CITY. DAYS LATER...

COMMANDER PETROVA?

PART II

WOLVES AGAINST THE STORM

FUCK OFF BACK TO YOUR CHOIRBOYS, VARGAS! THE NEW CONGREGATION ANSWER TO NO ONE BUT HIS *UNHOLINESS.*

AND FOR THE LAST TWENTY YEARS, HIS UNHOLINESS HAS WANTED THE HEAD OF THE *OLD* CONGREGATION'S MOST FEARED AGENT.

ONLY THEN WILL THE WEEDS OF HUMAN RESISTANCE FINALLY WITHER AND DIE.

A FEW SURVIVORS SCATTERED ABOUT THE GLOBE ARE THE *LEAST* OF OUR CONCERNS RIGHT NOW, VARGAS. WERE YOU NOT *LISTENING* WHEN I EXPLAINED WHAT'S COMING FOR US...?

THE ONLY *MONSTER* WE SEE ON OUR DOORSTEP, SIGNORA PETROVA, IS *THIS* ONE...

DID HE NOT MURDER THE *GREAT COUNT?* HE OF YOUR OWN *BLOOD?* NOT TO MENTION *COUNTLESS* OF OUR KIN SINCE THEN?

O *BLOOD,* MADE OF GOD...

EXACTLY WHY WE *NEED* HIM, CARDINAL!

I *BLESS* YOU...

IN NOMINE PATRIS ET FILII ET SPIRITUS SANCTI...

BALAUR HAS ARISEN!

HOW?

THE MASK OF RESURRECTION. IT TURNED UP AT AN ANTIQUES DEALER IN NORWAY. MY BROTHER'S FOLLOWERS STOLE IT AND USED IT TO BRING HIM BACK.

THAT WAS THREE DAYS AGO. WE'VE BEEN UNABLE TO TRACK HIM SINCE AND HAVE NO IDEA WHAT HE'S PLANNING TO DO NEXT.

HEH! YOU *MURDERED* HIM AND NOW YOU WANT ME TO *PROTECT* YOU FROM HIM...

YOU KNOW WHAT HE IS, VAN HELSING. AND YOU KNOW THAT UNLESS YOU HELP ME STOP HIM THERE WON'T BE A WORLD LEFT FOR *ANYONE* TO SAVE.

NOW STOP YOUR FUCKING PARLOUR TRICKS AND HELP US BEFORE I HAVE TO *KILL* YOU...

SSSSS!

SSSSS!

AND THEN THERE'S *THIS*.

IT'S A *UV FLASHBANG GRENADE*.

WE'VE SPENT *MILLIONS* DEVELOPING THE MERCURY DIFFUSER TO ACHIEVE AN EFFECTIVE KILL-RADIUS.

I MADE ONE OF THOSE OUT OF A *SODA CAN* LAST WEEK.

AND IT'S *RECHARGEABLE*.

VAN HELSING, YOU'VE REFUSED OUR OFFER OF FOOD AND A SHOWER, AND I ASSURE YOU WE'RE ALL *VERY* IMPRESSED BY YOUR RESOLVE. BUT WILL YOU AT *LEAST* TAKE A PROPER FIELD KIT!

THANK YOU, MADAM PETROVA. BUT I'VE SURVIVED LONG ENOUGH AND *KILLED* ENOUGH WITHOUT THE NEED FOR EXPENSIVE TOYS.

YOU THINK *ARROGANCE* WILL HELP YOU KILL MY BROTHER? I SINCERELY HOPE YOU'VE READ HIS FILE LIKE I ASKED.

BEFORE YOU DEVILS TOOK OVER THE CONGREGATION, I MADE A HABIT OF *MEMORISING* EVERY FILE I READ.

I DOUBT YOU'VE ADDED ANYTHING TO THE TWO PAGES THAT WERE IN THERE LAST TIME I LOOKED...

"SO PLEASE CORRECT ME IF I'M WRONG, MADAM...

"'BALAUR' – TRANSYLVANIAN SAXON FOR 'DRAGON' – WAS SIRED SOMEWHERE IN THE CARPATHIANS CIRCA EARLY 15TH CENTURY. HE IS OF THE PETROVA BLOODLINE, BUT MIXED WITH...

"SOMETHING ELSE.

"HIS TRUE NAME AND ORIGIN ARE A MYSTERY EVEN TO ME.

"HIS LEGEND WAS BORN OUT OF BATTLING THE OTTOMAN TURKS ALONGSIDE *THE IMPALER*, HIS BLOODLUST UNQUENCHABLE.

"WAR WAS THE ONLY THING THAT COULD CONTAIN HIM. HE WAS A FORCE OF NATURE, AN ELEMENTAL, A FIRE THAT KNOWS NOTHING EXCEPT HOW TO BURN.

HE WANDERED THE CONTINENT, DRAWN WHEREVER THE FIGHTING WAS THICKEST, BATTLING THE ENEMY ONE DAY AND HIS ALLIES THE NEXT.

"EVEN TURNING UPON *HIS OWN* FOR THE SAKE OF AN HOUR'S COMBAT.

"SO THE HOUSE OF PETROVA SENT HIS SWEET SISTER ATHENA TO REASON WITH HIM...

"ACCOMPANIED BY SEVERAL FRIENDS.

"THE HOLY MEN *BLESSED* YOUR BROTHER'S ARMOUR.

"AND, WELL, I'M SURE YOU CAN REMEMBER THE DETAILS OF THAT ENCOUNTER BETTER THAN I...

UTTH!

"THE LEGENDS SAID THAT BALAUR'S JAWBONE WAS THE ONLY PART OF HIS UNHOLY FORM NOT BURNED TO ASH BY THE SUN.

"AND THAT A CULT OF FOLLOWERS WHO CALLED THEMSELVES 'THE SONS OF BALAUR' FOUND IT SEVERAL DAYS LATER.

"THEY PRESERVED THIS RELIC INSIDE A MASK ENGRAVED WITH GLYPHS OF RESURRECTION... EARLY NEMORTIAN, IF I RECALL CORRECTLY.

"BUT THEY LOST THIS PRECIOUS BAUBLE BEFORE THEY COULD BRING HIM BACK TO UNLIFE AND HAVE BEEN SEARCHING FOR IT EVER SINCE.

MASK OF BALAUR

"NOW IT SEEMS THEIR PERSISTENCE HAS FINALLY BEEN REWARDED."

I DON'T RECALL ANYTHING IN THAT FILE ABOUT *THE RITE OF ASCENSION.*

THE SONS OF BALAUR ARE SAID TO HAVE SPENT CENTURIES SEARCHING FOR A WAY TO GRANT THEIR MASTER SOME KIND OF *KINGLY POWER* UPON HIS RETURN.

I HOPE THE PROSPECT OF AN ALL-POWERFUL VAMPIRE MADMAN WAS ONE TAKEN *SERIOUSLY* SINCE YOU TOOK OVER THE CONGREGATION...

WE'VE HAD BETTER THINGS TO DO THAN OBSESS OVER FOLK TALES, VAN HELSING. BALAUR'S RETURN IS SOMETHING NONE OF US COULD HAVE PREDICTED.

'BETTER THINGS'?

LIKE *SLAUGHTERING* MY PEOPLE AND ENSURING THE *EXTINCTION* AND *ENSLAVEMENT* OF HUMANITY? YOU SHOULD BEWARE, MADAM...

YOUR *SINGLE-MINDEDNESS* MAY PROVE TO BE YOUR DOWNFALL.

HAHAHA! YOUR GIFTS ARE MANY, MAN OF GOD. BUT A SENSE OF *IRONY* ISN'T AMONG THEM.

NOW THAT YOU'VE FINISHED CHECKING YOUR EQUIPMENT FOR TRACKING DEVICES, HAVE YOU WONDERED AT ALL WHY WE'RE LETTING YOU BACK INTO THE FIELD *ALONE?*

BECAUSE YOU KNOW I'LL *KILL* ANYONE YOU SEND WITH ME THE FIRST CHANCE I GET.

WELL, THAT TOO. BUT REMEMBER THAT *TRACER* IN YOUR BLOOD? I'M GUESSING YOU WERE THINKING OF FLUSHING IT OUT WITH SOME KIND OF *TRANSFUSION,* YES?

THE TRUTH IS IT'S NOW *BONDED* WITH YOUR DNA. *PERMANENTLY.* WE CAN FIND YOU NOW *WHEREVER* YOU ARE IN THE WORLD.

OR YOU COULD BE *LYING.*

RUN AND YOU'LL FIND OUT.

BUT DO YOU *REALLY* WANT TO SPEND THE REST OF YOUR DAYS BEING *HUNTED?* SOILING YOUR VEINS WITH STOLEN BLOOD 'TIL GOD ALMIGHTY *FINALLY* DECIDES TO END YOUR MISERY?

YOU'RE WELCOME.

MY PEOPLE WILL ESCORT YOU TO YOUR PLANE.

CALL ME ONCE YOU'VE SPOKEN TO YOUR CONTACT. I WANT TO KNOW WHAT WE'RE DEALING WITH AS SOON AS POSSIBLE.

GODSPEED, VAN HELSING.

WARSAW.

I SAW *FIRST-HAND* THE AGONIES OF ITS PAST.

'SEMPER INVICTA'.

CAW!

'EVER INVINCIBLE'.

SUCH LIFE.

SO MANY VOICES.

I CAN SEE NOW WHY *THE NAMELESS* CHOSE TO SETTLE HERE.

WELL, VERMIN? AM I TO BREAK YOUR *OTHER* ARM...?

HHNN... WASN'T US... *WE* DIDN'T KILL HIM...

"WE COULD SMELL THE FOOD THE BIRDS WERE BRINGING HIM...

"WE WERE WAITING FOR HIM TO SLEEP SO WE COULD EAT WHAT WAS LEFT...

"THEN THE OTHER MONSTER CAME...

"A *BLOOD-DRINKER.* THE *BIGGEST* I'VE EVER SEEN.

"THEY DIDN'T SPEAK...

"THEY JUST FOUGHT...

"WHEN HE ATE THE MONSTER'S HEART THERE WAS A SOUND LIKE THUNDER BREAKING...

"LIKE... LIKE THE VAMPIRE WAS DRINKING THE HEART OF A STORM...

"A STORM
THAT SOMEHOW
BECAME...

"PART OF HIM."

HAAA!!

FOOOSH

MASTER, ARE YOU HURT?

MASTER?

READ.

YES. YES, OF COURSE...

AUDIRE EVOCATIONEM MEAM, TENEBRIS DEOS AMBULANT DAMNATORUM REGNA...

"YOU SAID THE BOY WAS READING FROM A BOOK, GHOUL.

"CAN YOU REMEMBER *ANYTHING* OF WHAT HE SAID?"

IT SOUNDED LIKE HE WAS *CALLING* SOMETHING, SAID IT OVER AND OVER...

UH... TENEBRAY DAY US...

TENEBRIS DEOS...

THE DARK GODS. THE PANTHEON OF MONSTERS.

HE'S PERFORMING *THE RITE OF HEARTS!*

THE *WHAT?*

IT'S MAYAN BLOOD MAGIC. THE WORDS OF THE INCANTATION EXISTED ONLY IN FRAGMENTS. THE SONS OF BALAUR MUST HAVE PIECED THEM TOGETHER.

IT IS THROUGH THIS RITUAL THAT THEY WILL GRANT THEIR MASTER POWER OVER THE WORLD...

"THROUGH AIR AND EARTH...

"FIRE AND BLOOD...

"MEIN GOTT! WE MAY HAVE LOST *ALREADY*, MADAM PETROVA...

"BALAUR IS HIMSELF A BEING OF PURE BLOODLUST AND HAS ALREADY KILLED THE NAMELESS AND, NO DOUBT BY NOW, THE SHIFTER KING IN THE WEST.

"THEIR ELEMENTAL POWERS ARE NOW *HIS* TO COMMAND.

"HE HAS *ONE MORE* HEART LEFT TO CONSUME BEFORE HE HAS POWER ENOUGH TO CONSUME THE *WORLD!*"

FORTUNATELY, I THINK I KNOW TO WHOM THAT FINAL HEART MAY BELONG...

PART III

BROKEN SAINTS

AGENT VAN HELSING HAS ARRIVED IN CAIRO, COMMANDER.

ANY WORD FROM AIRSPACE?

NOTHING YET.

"BUT WE'RE COVERING THE WHOLE OF SOUTHERN EUROPE AND NORTH AFRICA, AS WELL AS EVERY DOCK AND AIRPORT.

THE SONS OF THE DRAGON SCREEEEEEEAM! HAHAHAHA HAHA!

"HE'S GOING TO HAVE TO GET PRETTY *CREATIVE* IF HE WANTS TO SLIP THE NET."

THE SHAPESHIFTER WILL HAVE GIVEN HIM A GOOD FIGHT. MAY EVEN HAVE *KILLED* HIM.

BUT EVEN IF HE'S *NOT* LICKING HIS WOUNDS AND FOUND A TRANSPORT WITH *SUN-COVER*, WE'LL STILL BE AT LEAST THREE HOURS AHEAD OF HIM.

MORE THAN ENOUGH TIME TO EXTRACT OUR FRIENDLY.

"REMIND THE TEAM THAT SHE LIKES FORMALITIES.

"TELL *VAN HELSING* HE'S GOING TO HAVE TO GO THROUGH WHATEVER DIVA BULLSHIT HE HAS TO GO THROUGH.

"SHE'S *VOLATILE* AT THE BEST OF TIMES. SO BUY HER FLOWERS, TONGUE HER ARSEHOLE, WHATEVER IT TAKES TO GET HER ON THAT FUCKING PLANE.

"WE CAN'T AFFORD ANY DELAYS."

THE QUEEN, SHE SAYS SHE WANTS TO SEE THE OLD MAN *ALONE* FIRST.

SHE'S GOT *FIVE MINUTES.*

SHE GOT AS LONG AS SHE FUCKIN' *WANTS,* MAN.

SEE YOU IN *FIVE MINUTES,* YOU PIECE'A SHIT...

"AND DON'T FORGET TO BE *NICE,* HUH?"

QUEEN NEMETARI, HONOURED BRIDE OF RA... THE WORLD IS IN PERIL FROM A *LEGENDARY* HORROR.

THIS CREATURE WOULD SEEK TO KILL YOU AND DEVOUR YOUR IMMORTAL HEART TO GAIN SOVEREIGNTY OVER THE SUN.

THE NEW CONGREGATION THEREFORE INSISTS YOU ACCEPT THEIR OFFER OF HOSPITALITY AND PROTECTION UNTIL THIS MATTER IS RESOLVED...

HMMMM

YOU SMELL LIKE A CAMEL'S ASSHOLE, MAN.

HAHAHAHA

GIVE YOUR ESTY, —

WHAT IS THIS BULLSHIT, MAN? SHE PROTECTS ME BY SENDING THE WORLD'S MOST FAMOUS KILLER TO MY DOOR? WHAT THE FUCK IS THAT, HUH?

DON'T I KEEP EVERY *BALTAGIYA* IN THE REGION OFF THEIR BACKS? DON'T I KEEP THEIR FUCKIN' SUPPLY ROUTES OPEN FOR THEM? THIS IS *DISRESPECT*, MAN.

AND HOW COME GOD'S HOLY ASSHOLE IS NOW WORKING FOR THE BLOODSUCKERS? I'M GONNA SIT *RIGHT* HERE UNTIL YOU TELL ME, OLD MAN...

I UNDERSTAND YOUR CAUTION, YOUR MAJESTY.

MY ALLIANCE WITH THE VAMPIRES IS INDEED INCREDIBLE, BUT I'M AFRAID GOD WILLS IT, HOWEVER UNSAVOURY THE EXPERIENCE MAY BE FOR ME.

IBN EL SHARMOOTA! YOU THINK MY PEOPLE SHUFFLE AROUND IN BANDAGES LIKE AN OLD MAN WITH SHIT IN HIS PANTS, HAH?

YOUR MASTERS THINK I'M AN EASY FUCKING KILL? IS THIS WHAT YOU'RE TELLING ME, MAN? I KILLED ASSASSINS FOR THE PHARAOHS *TWO-THOUSAND* YEARS BEFORE THE VIRGIN SHAT YOUR CHRIST INTO EXISTENCE!

KUSS UMMAK, YOU STINKING DOGFUCKER!

URrr...

DEAL WITH HIS PEOPLE. GET RID OF THE CAR. TAKE CARE OF THE SENTRIES. PETROVA WILL HAVE THEM CREEPING AROUND ALL OVER THE PLACE.

...W-WAIT! LISTEN TO ME!

THEY WANT YOU ALIVE. YOU... YOU ARE A *VALUABLE* ASSET TO THEM.

I'M JUST A MAN WHO DOESN'T BELIEVE IN TAKING CHANCES... UHN...

BALAUR *IS* COMING FOR YOU. AND WHEN HE FINDS YOU, HE WILL DRINK YOUR HEART'S BLOOD AND WALK UNIMPEDED ACROSS THE EARTH, KILLING ALL IN HIS PATH.

SPARE THE REST OF MY TEAM! FOR THE SAKE OF YOURSELF AND ALL YOU HAVE BUILT, YOUR MAJESTY. YOU *MUST* GO WITH THEM!

WE'VE JUST LOST CONTACT WITH VAN HELSING.

COMMANDER...

WE'VE LOST CONTACT WITH THE *ENTIRE* TEAM!

HRROOOOOOOOO!

GRR

HRN

ARR

A GOOD THING IT IS THAT I'VE BEEN DEAD FOR 4,000 YEARS!

BBRRMMMMMMMMM

AH, THE WARM-UP ACT.

I SEARCHED FOR ANSWERS.

AND FOUND A CURE.

BUT LOST A WIFE.

A MAN OF REASON SUDDENLY ADRIFT IN A SEA OF MARVELS.

THE MIRACULOUS HAD BECOME UNQUESTIONABLY *REAL*.

AND THE CRAVING FOR MORE ANSWERS BEGAN, THE QUEST OF THE POWERLESS MAN SEEKING POWER OVER HIS WORLD.

MY KNOWLEDGE BECAME A FORMIDABLE WEAPON, FORMIDABLE ENOUGH TO TOPPLE *KINGS* OF DARKNESS.

THUS THE SON OF A BOOKKEEPER BECAME A *LEGEND*, STRIKING TERROR INTO THE HEART OF TERROR ITSELF.

I TOOK MORE THAN PRIDE IN MY WORK... I TOOK...

I TOOK...

PLEASURE

A RUTHLESS SATISFACTION IN THE CERTAINTY THAT ANOTHER HORROR HAD BEEN EXTINGUISHED, WINNING ANOTHER FRACTION OF CONTROL OVER THE CHAOS OF THE WORLD.

NO! I TOOK NO PLEASURE IN THIS! I WAS DOING *GOD'S* WORK!

GOD'S WORK OR *MY OWN?*

IT WAS FAITH! *DUTY!*

HAH! MASKS I WORE TO CONCEAL THE *TRUTH!* COWARDLY EXCUSES TO COMMIT ATROCITIES THAT SATISFIED MY OWN DESIRES!

IGNORE THE VOICES! THEY ARE CONJURED BY NEMETARI'S CURSED MASK! THEY ARE NOT MY OWN!

I FEEL ANOTHER TREMOR AS TITANS BATTLE ABOVE ME. THE WALL GIVES WAY BESIDE ME. I THROW MY WEIGHT AGAIN.

UMF!

FORGIVE ME, LORD.

UHNNN!

KRONCH!

I LOVE YOU AND ONLY YOU! I BELIEVE IN YOU AND ONLY YOU!

I BELIEVE IN MYSELF! IN THE TRUTH!

I PINCH THE SCAR ON MY ARM UNTIL THE FLESH POPS WET BETWEEN MY FINGERS.

THEN I FUMBLE FOR THE KEY TO MY SALVATION.

THE CHAMBER WILL COLLAPSE ANY SECOND!

WILL GOD CHOOSE TO END MY LIFE HERE OR DOES HE *STILL* HAVE WORK FOR ME?

THE CHOICE IS *MINE* NOT HIS! *FUCK HIM!*

I ALONE HAVE *CHOSEN* TO ENDURE!

THERE IS *NO ONE* TO LOVE OR HATE BUT *MYSELF.*

A MARTYRDOM OF MY OWN MAKING.

GOD HAS NOT ABANDONED ME... *HE WAS NEVER THERE!*

CLICK

I AM FREE!

DAMN THIS MASK!

SPAK!

THESE BLASPHEMIES ARE *NOT* MINE! THEY...

THIRTY MINUTES LATER.

AREA SECURE.

THE CREATURE FLEW ON ALONE.

WHERE'S THE BOY?

FUCK'S WRONG WITH *HIM?*

JUST GET HIM INSIDE.

I... I KNOW YOU'LL *SAVE* ME, MASTER...

I KNOW YOU CAN HEAR MY PRAYERS.

I'M *NOT* AFRAID.

I HAVE FAITH.

PART IV

TWILIGHT OF THE GODLESS

AN HOUR LATER...

WHERE *IS* SHE?

WHEN SHE ORDERED AN *EVACUATION*, I ASSUMED SHE WOULDN'T INCLUDE *HERSELF*.

ON THE CONTRARY, CARDINAL VARGAS. SHE'S ON HER WAY TO *PORT AVIOLTO*.

FROM THERE SHE'S TAKING A PRIVATE VESSEL AND WILL BE ENGAGING THE TARGET AT SEA *BEFORE* HE CAN REACH HERE.

ONCE ENGAGED, OUR SUBS WILL DESTROY THE VESSEL AND *EVERYONE* ON BOARD. WE HAVE JETS ON A CARRIER NEARBY THAT WILL MOP UP ANY RESISTANCE.

EVER THE *DIVA*, OUR LITTLE MISS PETROVA...

"ONCE AGAIN, THE *SIMPLEST* SOLUTION ELUDES HER..."

WHAT ARE YOU DOING *HERE*?

I ORDERED ALL NON-ESSENTIAL STAFF TO *LEAVE!* WHY AREN'T YOU ARSEHOLES *ESCORTING* THEM?

I'M SORRY, COMMANDER. YOU NEED TO COME WITH US...

"ALL UNITS HAVE BEEN ORDERED TO *HOLD BACK*. WE DON'T WANT TO PROVOKE HIM BEFORE HE REACHES COMMANDER PETROVA..."

NOW, CARDINAL. IF YOU DON'T MIND. I HAVE TO—

I'D LIKE YOU TO SCRAMBLE JETS TO INTERCEPT THE TARGET *IMMEDIATELY*.

I'M SORRY...?

CARDINAL, WITH ALL DUE RESPECT...

COMMANDER *PETROVA* IS IN CHARGE OF THIS DEPARTMENT.

CAPTAIN, MAY I SPEAK TO MADAM PETROVA...? OR IS SHE NOT IN THE MOOD FOR TALKING RIGHT NOW...?

CAPTAIN...?

UHNN...

FORGIVE ME, LIEUTENANT.

COULD YOU POSSIBLY OPEN A CHANNEL FOR ME?

AHEM!

ATTENTION, ALL AIR CREWS. THIS IS *CARDINAL VARGAS.*

DUE TO HER *DISGRACEFUL* LACK OF JUDGEMENT IN ALLOWING HER OPERATIVE TO COMPROMISE OUR PROCEDURES IN THE MIDDLE EAST, THE COUNCIL HAS DECIDED TO *COURT-MARTIAL* COMMANDER ATHENA PETROVA.

PLEASE *IGNORE* ANY PREVIOUS ORDERS YOU MAY HAVE RECEIVED FROM HER.

VARGAS, WHAT ARE YOU DOING?

AS OF NOW, *I* AM CONGREGATION COMMANDER AND HEAD OF SECURITY, AND AS SUCH I ORDER THE IMMEDIATE *ARREST* OF MADAM PETROVA...

NNNGH!

EEEAAGH!

EXCELLENT. THAT'S *ONE* LESS COMPLICATION WE HAVE TO DEAL WITH.

NOW, ABOUT THOSE *JETS*, LIEUTENANT...

Y-YES, *COMMANDER*...

NO LIGHTNING BOLTS, *BROTHER*? NO HOWLS OF TRANSFORMATION?

HOPING TO TAKE YOUR TIME, HUH?

TAKE MY PASS-KEY. DO WHATEVER THE *FUCK* YOU'RE GOING TO DO WITH IT, VAN HELSING. IT MAKES NO DIFFERENCE NOW

JUST... JUST *LEAVE* ME.

I *AM*... I AM GOING... TO MAKE YOU... *HOLLOW*. WITH MY *HANDS*. I WILL *WEAR* YOU...

SMOTHER MYSELF IN YOU WHILE YOU *WATCH*...

FILL THE SKIES WITH YOUR *SCREAMS!*

IN MOST SPECIES, OVER 40% OF THEIR BRAIN IS DEVOTED TO THEIR SENSE OF *SMELL*.

WHILE THE OTHER 60% IS DEVOTED TO SATISFYING THEIR UNNATURAL *HUNGER*.

WHICH MAKES THEM *SURPRISINGLY* EASY TO ELUDE.

ESPECIALLY WHEN ONE TAKES THE PRECAUTION OF FILLING THEIR POCKETS WITH FRESH WEREWOLF FAECES.

I THINK I LEARNED *THAT* TRICK DURING AN OPERATION IN THE UKRAINE.

LONG AGO. IN ANOTHER LIFE.

I HAVEN'T BEEN IN *HERE* IN OVER A DECADE.

EVERYTHING'S BEEN MOVED.

EXCEPT WHAT I'M LOOKING FOR...

AS THOUGH THE NEW VAULTKEEPERS *FEARED* TO TOUCH IT...

AND WITH *GOOD* REASON.

FATHER WAS *WRONG* ABOUT YOU, BALAUR.

THE *TRUTH* IS YOU WOULDN'T BURN HALF AS *BRIGHT* IF YOU DIDN'T *CARE*.

HE *KNEW* YOUR BLOOD WAS CORRUPTED. HE *MISTOOK* YOU FOR A MAD DOG, THE FIRE THAT KNOWS NOTHING EXCEPT HOW TO BURN, YES?

YOU'RE TOO *DUMB* TO KNOW IT, BUT YOU *HAVEN'T* FORGOTTEN WHY YOU'RE BURNING IN THE FIRST PLACE, HAVE YOU?

RUNNCH!

YOU *BETRAYED* ME!

DENIED ME THIS WORLD FOR *CENTURIES*!

AND WHY DO YOU *GIVE* A FUCK?

YOU RISKED YOUR NEWFOUND EXISTENCE, FACED THE WORLD'S *GREATEST* HORRORS JUST TO GET BACK AT *ME*? WHY?

BECAUSE *I'M* THE ONE WHO *MADE* YOU BEFORE I *KILLED* YOU — AND NEITHER BY *CHOICE*...

YOU REMEMBER WHAT YOU ONCE *WERE*, DON'T YOU?

IT'S STILL IN THERE ISN'T IT? *BURIED* BENEATH THE HUNGER AND THE RAGE. IT'S IN THAT *YEARNING* FOR THE OLD WORLD.

MAYBE YOU *DO* HAVE BRAINS ENOUGH TO KNOW THAT ONCE YOU'VE SCORCHED *THIS* WORLD OF LIFE AND DRIVEN YOURSELF TO STARVATION, YOU STILL WON'T HAVE REPLACED WHAT YOU *LOST*!

HAKK!

THAT YOU'RE EVEN *LISTENING* TO ME TELLS ME I'M RIGHT.

DOES HE RECOGNISE IT?

THE ARMOUR HE WORE THE DAY HIS SISTER MURDERED HIM!

SANCTIFIED BY THE BLESSINGS OF A DOZEN LIVING SAINTS, ITS AURA A WARD AGAINST EVIL.

ITS MEREST TOUCH A *SCOURGE* UPON THE DAMNED.

SELF-HYPNOSIS BLOCKS MUCH OF THE PAIN...

BUT NOT THE SMELL OF MY OWN FLESH *CRISPING*, SIZZLING LIKE MEAT IN THE PAN.

MY COURAGE THREATENS TO ABANDON ME.

EEEAARGH!

SACRED BULLETS.

UNFORTUNATELY, I HAD NO TIME TO SNATCH ANY *OTHER* SUCH TRINKETS FROM THE VAULT.

NOW I MUST IMPROVISE.

SHRAKBOOM

YAIEEE!

SHRA KOOOM

UNHARMED, BUT BLINDED...

HNNGH!

NOW TO—

SPAK!

NOTHING LEFT.

NO MORE TRICKS. NO HEAVENLY REASSURANCES.

CLONK

HE DOESN'T GIVE ME THE CHANCE TO RUN THIS TIME.

I'M LASHING OUT LIKE A CORNERED ANIMAL, CHOKING ON THE BLOOD IN MY THROAT, SPLINTERED BONE STABBING MY INSIDES.

MY MANTRA FALTERS – AN *INFERNO* OF PAIN CONSUMES ME.

AAAAARGH

THIS IS *NOT* HOW MY LEGEND WILL END.

FLAILING LIKE AN OVERTURNED TORTOISE.

UGH!

KNOW THIS...

BEFORE I DIE, I WILL ENSURE YOU *REMEMBER* ME...

FUCKER!

MY ARMOURED FINGERS CLUTCHING AT HIS LIFELESS ORGANS, GROPING FOR HIS HEART.

AAAAH!

SHUCK!

I HAVE BEEN FED UPON BEFORE BUT NEVER WITH SUCH *FEROCITY*, EVERY PULL DRAINING WHAT FEELS LIKE AN *OCEAN* OF BLOOD.

I HEAR MYSELF COMMENCE A NEW MANTRA...

I AM ALBERIC VAN HELSING.

FIGHTER...

KILLER...

SPLATCH

SSSSss

PYE'S SKETCHBOOK

COVER ART PROGRESSION

PENCILS

FINAL ART

INKS

THE NAMELESS

Van Helsing

Nemetari

BALAUR

CHARACTER PENCILS

PYE'S
SKETCHBOOK

VEHICLE
PENCILS

PYE'S
SKETCHBOOK

Blood & Beer!

REALM OF THE DAMNED

MERCHANDISE

REALM OF THE DAMNED 1 & 2

REALM OF THE DAMNED 3 & 4

REALM OF THE DAMNED 5

VAN HELSING VAMPIRES

BALAUR SCREAM

BALAUR FEEDS

SONS OF BALAUR - TENEBRIS DEOS

REALM OF THE DAMNED 6